SERIES EDITOR
TERRY VIRGO

How to...

STUDY SERIES

BEING SURE
OF THE BIBLE

ARNOLD BELL

WORD PUBLISHING

WORD (UK) Ltd
Milton Keynes, England

WORD AUSTRALIA
Kilsyth, Victoria, Australia
WORD COMMUNICATIONS LTD
Vancouver, B.C., Canada
STRUIK CHRISTIAN BOOKS (PTY) LTD
Maitland, South Africa
ALBY COMMERCIAL ENTERPRISES PTE LTD
Balmoral Road, Singapore
CHRISTIAN MARKETING NEW ZEALAND LTD
Havelock North, New Zealand
JENSCO LTD
Hong Kong
SALVATION BOOK CENTRE
Malaysia

BEING SURE OF THE BIBLE

© Arnold Bell 1990.
Published by Word (UK) Ltd/New Frontiers.

ISBN 0-85009-187-X (Australia ISBN 1-86258-125-8)

The quotation on page 38 by John Wenham is taken from *The Lion Handbook to the Bible* edited and produced by David and Pat Alexander, Lion Publishing, 1973.

Typeset by Phoenix Manor, Milton Keynes and printed and bound in Great Britain by Clays Ltd, St Ives plc

FOREWORD

The "How to" series has been published with a definite purpose in view. It provides a set of workbooks suitable either for housegroups or individuals who want to study a particular Bible theme in a practical way. The goal is not simply to look up verses and fill in blank spaces on the page, but to fill in gaps in our lives and so increase our fruitfulness and our knowledge of God.

Peter wrote his letters to "stimulate wholesome thinking" (2 Peter 3:1). He required his readers to think as well as read! We hope the training manual approach of this book will have the same effect. *Stop, think, apply* and *act* are key words.

If you are using the book on your own, we suggest you work through the chapters systematically, Bible at your side and pen in hand. If you are doing it as a group activity, it is probably best to do all the initial reading and task work before the group sessions — this gives more time for discussion on key issues which may be raised.

Unless otherwise stated, all quotations from the Bible are from the New International Version which you are, in the main, encouraged to use when you fill in the study material.

Terry Virgo
Series Editor

FRONTIER PUBLISHING INTERNATIONAL is committed to the production of printed and recorded materials with a view to reaching this generation with the gospel of the Kingdom. FPI is a part of New Frontiers International, a team ministry led by Terry Virgo, which is involved in planting and equipping churches according to New Testament principles. New Frontiers International is also responsible for a wide range of training programmes and conferences.

Contents

About This Book   9

Lesson 1   God Reveals Who He Is   11

Lesson 2   An Inspired Book   17

Lesson 3   The Authority of Scripture   25

Lesson 4   Facing Up to Difficulties   35

Lesson 5   As Originally Given?   45

Lesson 6   So What?   51

Lesson 7   Keeping Our Bearings   59

Lesson 8   Getting Down to It   67

When Paul could foresee trouble ahead for the church in Ephesus, his remedy was to commit the elders of the church to God and to "the word of his grace, which can build you up and give you an inheritance among all those who are sanctified." (Acts 20:32)

The danger of God's people being led astray is no less today; indeed, the possibility will increase as the last days approach. The safeguard for us is the same as it was for the Ephesians of the first century: God and His Word.

But what if we relegate the Bible to a secondary position in our thinking? What if we have picked up the doubts and misconceptions about the Bible that are common in the world around us? What if we rely more heavily on our own sense of God's leading than we do on what is written in Scripture? Where is our defence then against deception?

Being Sure of the Bible has been produced to be put into the hands of the ordinary members of the church. It is envisaged that housegroups could use it for an eight-week programme of teaching to help people to come to a clearer understanding of the unique authority and importance of the Bible. Obviously, in such a setting, the leader can add to the "bare bones" offered here according to the needs of the group.

Some may object that the "filling in the gaps" method adopted in these lessons is rather childish. It is! But it is worth doing nonetheless. It can be a marvellous help to one's thinking processes to have to stop and write out the key words of a passage.

The New International Version of the Bible has been used throughout. Some adjustments may be necessary if a different version is used, but no great difficulties should arise.

Lesson 1   GOD REVEALS WHO HE IS

1. Where We Start

We believe that the Bible is a revelation that God has given of Himself. Unless God had revealed Himself to man, we could not know anything at all about Him. Let's see first of all why that is so.

A. Who we are

We are small. The sheer vastness of the universe shows us how small we are. We know enough to know that the sum total of what man has explored and explained so far is only a tiny fraction of what there is to explore and explain. Since we know so little about creation, we are obviously unable to get beyond creation and discover the Creator.

We are human. There are many things that lie within our capability, but, equally, there are many things which do not. One thing which is quite beyond us is to investigate the existence of God, for God is Spirit. Look up and write out:

Job 11:7 ....

....

Job 37:23b ....

....

Can you prove the existence of God?   YES/NO

Of course you can be absolutely sure that God exists, but there is no way that you could have investigated and proved the existence of God all by yourself, for God has put Himself beyond our reach.

We are sinful. Not only is our search for God hampered by the limitations of being small and human, but worst of all — we are blindfold! Our rebellion

11

against God has rendered us incapable of seeing what is clear, so we certainly have no hope of seeing what is not clear.

Look up these references in the New Testament and write down what they tell us about our sinful condition:

Romans 1:21 ...*thinking futile + hearts darkened*...

....

....

1 Corinthians 1:21 ...*foolishness*...

....

....

2 Corinthians 4:4 ...*blind*..

....

....

B. Who God is

Even if we were somehow able to overcome all the problems that we have been looking at, we would still not be able to get to know God. Look up 1 Timothy 6:16 and write down the reason:

God lives in ...*unapproachable light, whom no one has seen or can see*...

....

The picture begins to look rather black, doesn't it? How can we know anything about God? Unless God were to reveal Himself to us, it would be quite impossible. And that is where the rest of the truth about who God is comes in: for God is a Person, who made us and loves us, and so we can reasonably expect that He would also communicate with us. And He has ...!

2. God Shows Himself to Us

If we want to find out about somebody it is not too difficult to find someone who knows them and ask questions. We might well discover things about them that they would not wish us to know. But, as we have seen, we are in no position to subject God to this kind of investigation. We can only know what He is willing to show us. The miracle, of course, is that we are allowed to know anything at all!

How, then, has God revealed Himself to us?

A. In a general way

God has revealed aspects of His nature in ways that are accessible to everybody.

The most obvious way that God has revealed Himself is **in the universe** that He has created. It may surprise you to learn just how much we can know about God from looking at what He has made.

Read through these verses from the Bible, and write down the various things that they say we should know about God from creation:

Psalm 19:1...... *Glory of God* ....

Acts 14:17 ...... *Kindness* ....

Romans 1:20... *eternal power o divine nature* ...

We can see enough about the character of God in what He has made to "seek Him, and perhaps reach out for Him and find Him" (Acts 17:27). Sadly, this is not what mankind has normally done. Those whose only glimpse of God is through His handiwork all around them have generally chosen to worship something that they can see rather than the One who made it all. This is why people have no excuse before God (see Romans 1:20-23).

A second way God has shown something about Himself to everyone is by giving us all a sense of **conscience**. This sense of right and wrong might well be far short of God's standards, but its very existence is enough for us to know that it is necessary to do good, and this in turn should let us know that there is a God who requires this of us. Sadly, our consciences only have the effect of showing us we do wrong; they do not stir us to be holy and God is holy.

Read Romans 2:12-16. Do we need to have been taught the truths of the Bible before we can be held accountable to God? Why not?

(See verse 15) *the requirements of the law are written on their hearts*

Obviously, this general revelation of God can only achieve a limited amount. Because it is available to everybody wherever they are, it means that everybody is given an opportunity to acknowledge God. Our wilful rejection of even this limited revelation means that God can, with perfect justice, declare the human race guilty. This universal guilt is what makes evangelism such an essential priority.

However, unless God communicates with us in words we would be left in the dark concerning who God really is, and, more particularly, concerning His desire to save. These facts cannot be shown to us by the world about us; we need words from heaven. So that brings us to the second way God has revealed Himself to us ...

B. In a special way
Look at Hebrews 1:1,2, and find the two ways God has spoken to us:
1. "Through the .. *prophets* ......" 2. "By his *Son* ...."
The most special way that God has spoken from heaven is **by sending His Son** Jesus Christ into the world. It is because Jesus is a revelation of the Father that He is called "the Word" in John 1:1-14.

The second way that God has spoken to us is **by speaking through people**. God has not merely done things and left us to form our own conclusions. He has spoken in words that explain and define the significance of His actions. It is these words that we find in the Bible. The Bible is not just a human attempt to describe the encounters that men have had with God at various times, it is a revelation of God in words that He has given.

Because it is very important that we should be sure about it, we will look at some passages from the Bible that teach us about this vital matter.
● God has used words to communicate with man — see Exodus 31:18. God left His people in no doubt about His intentions. Not only did He speak with Moses, He even gave him a written form of His commandments!

14

- God is not content merely to do things; He speaks as well. Look up Exodus 33:18-19. What does Moses want God to do?

  show him his glory

  What does God say He will do?........... _proclaim His name_

  The glory of God is not just something that can be seen. The glory of God is His wonderful character — and that is best conveyed in words. Had these words not been uttered, Moses would have had a lesser understanding of God.

- When the prophets spoke, their words were actually God's words — see, for example, 2 Kings 17:13. Here God refers to the instructions He has given to His people. He did not speak with a voice out of the sky, He spoke through prophets. The prophets' words were God's words.

- God condemns the prophets whose words were not given directly by Him — see Jeremiah 23:16-32. Clearly we cannot assume that there is some kind of revelation in all "religious" utterances. God is very particular about what is said in His name. He doesn't tolerate what has not come accurately from Him.

- The Book of Job gives us a lengthy but devastating picture of the contrast between the words of those who are trying to convey their impression of God's will, and the words that God actually speaks. Isn't it good that God has given us not just muddled impressions that we have to sift and unravel, but His own words!

- In the New Testament, we see how Jesus committed a body of teaching to the apostles and told them to pass it on — see Matthew 28:20. What does this verse say that the apostles were to teach?

  "... everything _I have commanded_ you."

  God was speaking in Christ, and His words were to be faithfully passed on.

So we see that we have, in the Bible, a revelation of God given to us in words that He has spoken.

15

What We Have Learned So Far

God has revealed His existence, glory and goodness to us through His creation.

God has revealed His requirement of righteousness by giving us a conscience.

God has revealed His purposes, particularly with regard to salvation, in words specifically given by Him to us. These words, collected together, form our Bible.

How did they come to be written down? That is what we will be exploring in our next study.

We have seen that God has not only shown Himself to us through what He has made and by intervening in our lives; He has spoken. But how did those words come to be written down? And how can we be sure that the book which we know today as the Bible is an accurate version of what was written by many different people in different places and different ages?

To answer those questions, we need to think about what we mean when we call the Bible an inspired book.

1.   Inspiration — What Does It Mean?

A.   The key verse

> "All scripture is God-breathed and is useful for teaching, rebuking, correcting and training in righteousness ..."
> (2 Timothy 3:16)

NOTE: this translation gives a better sense of the meaning of the Greek word that is normally translated "inspired by God"; it is literally "God-breathed".

When we announce that we consider something that we have read to be "inspired", we are normally suggesting one of two things: either we are saying that we feel the author must have been inspired when he wrote it, or we are saying that the words we have read have inspired us.

When we say that the Bible is inspired, however, we do not necessarily mean either of these things. What we mean is that the words themselves were inspired, or "breathed out", by God.

We are saying nothing about the state of mind of the writers, nor of the effect of their words on us; we are simply saying that the words are words that God breathed out. They are a divine product.

17

When Paul refers to "all scripture", he means not only all the Old Testament; he would also be including the writings circulating amongst the churches that go to make up our New Testament, for, in his first letter (1 Tim 5:18) he quotes Luke 10:7 together with Deuteronomy 25:4 calling them both "the Scripture".

Look up 2 Peter 3:15-16. What does Peter include in the category of "Scriptures"?

............Paul's letter..

B. Inspiration and revelation

We don't want to get too technical, but it might be helpful to examine the difference between "revelation" and "inspiration". Revelation comes first: it is God revealing truth to man. Inspiration refers to the means by which that truth is committed to writing. Neither word is referring to those experiences that WE have when we come to a fresh understanding of a particular truth; they are referring to things that God did in the past that ensure that we can know the truth today.

To see the distinction between these two words think about this problem! Look up 1 Chronicles 1:1-54 and Isaiah 53:1-12. Read them carefully.

Now answer this question: which passage is most inspired, and which has most revelation?

....

The answer is that both passages are equally breathed out by God, for "all scripture is God-breathed ...". However, the Isaiah passage is clearly a greater revelation of God than the Chronicles passage.

There may be differences of revelation, but all is equally inspired.

2. The Inspiration of the Old Testament

You may be wondering whether our belief in the inspiration of the Bible depends on the correct interpretation of just one verse in 2 Timothy 3. Not at all. It is clear that both Old and New Testaments are written with an awareness of inspiration.

In the Old Testament:

- We read of men who knew their words came from God. What was the phrase that the prophets used to introduce their message? (See Exodus 5:1, Joshua 7:13, 2 Samuel 12:11.)

    This is what the Lord says

- The way God spoke through His servants the prophets is illustrated by the relationship between Moses and Aaron. Aaron was an effective speaker, so he acted as Moses' spokesman with Moses telling him what to say. This meant that it was as if Moses were God and Aaron the prophet. The prophet used his ability to communicate, but the content of his message was given to him by another — God. You can find this story about Moses in Exodus 4:14-17.

- There is absolutely no doubt about the fact that the law taught by Moses was the law of God. Obviously people were aware that it was Moses who had brought these words to the nation, but nonetheless they clearly identified the words of God's servant with the words of God. When Moses, or any other prophet, spoke, it was God speaking to His people.

    Look up and complete the following verses:

    Nehemiah 8:1b — "They told Ezra the scribe to bring out the Book of the Law of Moses, which *the Lord* had commanded for Israel."

    Jeremiah 25:4,7 — "And though the Lord has sent all his servants the prophets to you again and again, you have not listened or paid any attention ... But you did not listen to *me*," declares the Lord."

- A revelation of God and His purposes is given which Jesus accepted implicitly. Never did Jesus contradict or question anything recorded in the Old Testament. Indeed, His characteristic phrase is, "It is written ..."

    Further, we find Jesus identifying the words of the prophets as the words of God:

    "You have let go of the commands of *God* and are holding on to the traditions of *men*" (Mark 7:8)

Although the commands came through a man, Moses, they were divine in origin and could be contrasted with traditions that had a human source.

In one instance, we find Jesus referring explicitly to the fact of inspiration:

"David himself, speaking by the Holy Spirit, declared: ..." (Mark 12:36) David may have voiced the actual words, but their content was inspired by the Spirit of God.

The way Jesus regarded the Old Testament was followed by the apostles. For them, too, the Old Testament was God's word to man. Look up some of these references and see for yourself: Acts 1:16, 28:25; Romans 1:2, 9:25; Galatians 3:8 (in this interesting verse, Paul uses the word "Scripture" instead of "God" — you cannot have much clearer evidence than that that for the apostles the Scriptures were God speaking!); 2 Peter 2:20-21.

We will look later at the question of HOW God inspired these men, but for the present it is sufficient to conclude that the prophets, poets and historians whose words are found in the Old Testament were so influenced by the Holy Spirit that their words were in fact God's words.

3. The Inspiration of the New Testament

When we come to consider the inspiration of the New Testament the matter is much simpler. Basically we have to decide what we believe about Jesus. If we believe He is who He claimed to be, the Son of God, God become man, then we will also recognise that His words are God's words. Certainly, He taught that His words had a unique authority. Look up and complete the following:

John 6:63 — "The words I have spoken to you are ...Spirit... and they are ...life..."

John 8:38 — "I am telling you what I have seen in the Father's presence ..."

Mark 13:31 — "Heaven and earth will pass away, but ...my words... will never pass away."

Right at the start of His ministry, Jesus chose twelve men to be with Him as disciples. They were exposed to His teaching publicly and privately until the time of His ascension to heaven. Hence they were charged with the task of going to all nations, "teaching them to obey everything I have commanded you" (Matt 28:20).

Lest their memories should fail them and their account of Jesus' teaching be unreliable, Jesus gave them a special promise that would guarantee the accuracy of their ministry.

Look up John 14:15-26. Note what is promised in v.26:
"But the Counsellor, the Holy Spirit, whom my Father will send in my name, will teach you all things and will *remind you of everything* I have said to you."

See also John 16:13-15. What will the Holy Spirit do for the apostles?

He will speak *only what he hears*

He will tell *you what is yet to come*

He will take *from what is Jesus' & make it known to them*

Although he was not one of this original group, Paul was aware that he was called by God to be an apostle (Eph 1:1) and that as such he had come into the good of these promises given by Jesus (see Eph 3:4-5, 1 Tim 4:1).

The apostles were therefore able to say quite unselfconsciously that anyone with a genuine relationship with God would recognise and listen to the apostolic message (see 1 Cor 14:37-38, 1 John 4:6).

As we have seen, Paul quotes a saying of Jesus alongside one from Moses, calling both "Scripture" (1 Tim 5:18), while Peter goes further and implies that the letters of Paul are to be regarded as "Scripture" (2 Peter 3:16).

The claim of the New Testament to be inspired, then, rests on the claim of Jesus to be God the Son. Because He is God, not only His personal teaching but also that of those given a unique commission and anointing to spread His words can be said to be "God-breathed".

4. How Did It Happen?

We have seen that the Bible was inspired by God. We have explored what this means and discovered that it means that the words themselves were breathed out by God. But this raises some big questions! What part did the human authors play in it all? Were they in some sort of trance? Did they know what was happening? If their own faculties were involved, then surely errors could have crept in?

We cannot fully understand how it happened, any more than we can understand how Jesus could be fully human and fully divine, or how we can be saved only because God sovereignly chose us and yet also because we heard His word and repented of our sin. In all these cases we are confronted by something that can be explained as both all human and all divine — yet not a mixture of both!

Hard to understand it might be, but there are some things of which we can be sure:

A. Not dictation

It is sometimes assumed that those who believe in a divinely inspired Bible believe that it was dictated word by word, thus reducing its writers to the role of secretary. This is not what we believe.

It is quite clear from even a superficial reading of the Bible that this idea just does not fit the facts. We can see that the various writers each contribute their own style and personality to the books bearing their names. Often their words were penned in response to particular needs — as in the case of the epistles — or as the result of detailed research (see Luke 1:1-4).

God did not override their individuality, bypass their minds or cause words to flow from their pens by some kind of weird automatic process. No, their words were their own — and yet they were from God.

B. Not a mixture

What we find in the Bible is not the product of God somehow reducing His words to what would be reasonable for ordinary men with limited knowledge and a fair number of misconceptions to utter. It is not a mixture of divine truth and human errors — any more than Jesus is a mixture of Holy God and sinful man. He became a real man, yet without sin. So the Bible was really produced by ordinary men — yet without error. Thus Jesus was able to declare quite categorically, "The Scripture cannot be broken" (John 10:35).

C. A miracle

The only conclusion that fits the evidence is that God sovereignly ordered events and thoughts so that men spoke His word in a manner that reflected their background and personality while being free from error. It is this miracle that makes the Bible unique.

5. Is Every Word True?

If what was written was breathed out by God, it follows that the words used were the right ones to express God's mind. Often, however, people ask, "But is every word true?" Now this is really a rather silly question. You see, we believe that what we are saying in this booklet is true; but that does not mean that we are confident that every word *taken alone* is somehow "true". Truth is expressed by *words that fit together with other words*. In that context they convey truth — and the words in the Bible are the right ones to do this. Lift them out of their surroundings, and they might not be "true" any more. For example, Psalm 14:1 contains the words, "There is no God." Those words are not true taken out of context; they are only true when taken with the rest of the sentence which reads, "The fool says in his heart, 'There is no God'. "

6. How It Shows

If the Bible is what we have said it is, a book written by men but breathed out by God, then we would expect to see evidence of this as we read it. We do.

A. Prophecy is fulfilled

As you read the Old Testament, you cannot miss the tremendous amount of often quite detailed prophecy. It is quite breathtaking to see, for example, how the things that happened in the life of Jesus were foretold by the Old Testament prophets.

See how Matthew stresses this by looking up some of these verses: 2:5,15,17; 3:3; 4:14; 8:17; 12:17; 21:4.

It has been said that you can tell the story of Jesus without using the New Testament: it is all there in the Old. If you turn to Luke 24:25-27, you will see that Jesus Himself did this.

How could men speak out and write down details of events that had not yet happened? It was because their words were breathed out by God.

B. It's all the same book

The Bible consists of sixty-six books, and yet it is just one book. There is a remarkable harmony between these books as they combine to unfold the story of God's purposes. It is the same God that is spoken about throughout; in whichever book we meet Him we find the same terrible holiness and strong love. How can this be? It was the same Spirit speaking through different authors.

C. Unique insight

The subject matter of the Bible betrays its divine authorship. It tells us things that only a book given by God could tell us:

● What it tells us about the character of God and the nature of man makes us feel uncomfortable: it is telling the story from God's side, not ours.
● Its subject matter is too vast to have come from human minds. The Bible tells us how the world was made, and lifts the veil to show us something of how it will end.

None of this "proves" that the Bible is inspired. Nevertheless, if we accept that this book is breathed out by God, then we would expect to see evidence of this supernatural origin in its pages and these are some of the ways in which we find it.

What We Have Learned In This Lesson

While we may not understand how it happened, we can be sure that the Bible was written as the result of a supernatural work of God.

We can be sure, therefore, that what it says is true, that it says what God intended it to say, and is as reliable as God Himself.

How then should we regard it today? What place should it have in our decision-making, or in the forming of our opinions and beliefs? Those are the questions we turn to next.

1.　The Big Question

We have seen that the Bible is a unique book. It is a revelation of truth from God, given to us in words that He breathed out.

But the Bible has been with us for a long time now, and the world and its problems have changed out of all recognition since it was written.

How, then, should we regard the Bible today? Various answers have been given to this question, which fall into four broad categories:

A.　The "Catholic" view

The Bible has authority for the church, but it is not sufficient by itself. It has to be viewed in conjunction with the traditions of the church, and interpreted in the light of those traditions. In effect, this means that ultimate authority rests with the church. The church decides how the Bible should be understood, and bases its beliefs on its own traditions as well as, or instead of, the Bible.

B.　The "Liberal" view

Because the Bible was written by many different hands at different times and places, it is a book of uneven quality. It is affected by the lack of knowledge and the prejudices of its authors, and so the modern reader has to use his common sense to decide what has value for him and what can be put down to the ignorance of a bygone age. Some would say that if a passage does something for you, then that is its value; to discuss whether or not the passage is actually true is not relevant.

C. The "Fringe Charismatic" view

"The letter kills, but the Spirit gives life" (2 Cor 3:6b), therefore we should not keep quoting "dead" Scripture, but rather look for the "now" word of God. This could be either a prophecy or a passage of Scripture that is "quickened" to you. (Those who teach this point of view often draw a distinction between the two Greek words which are translated "word" in the New Testament: *logos* and *rhema*. *Logos*, they say, means the written word, while *rhema* is the spoken word, the word that is living and for now. In fact no such distinction can be made as these two words are used interchangeably in the New Testament.)

D. The "Evangelical" view

Because the Bible is the Word of God, it is our final authority in all matters relating to what we believe and how we act. We are not to judge it in the light of our reason or our experiences or traditions, for where there is any apparent disagreement between these and the Bible, it is the Bible that is reliable every time. We are to humbly acknowledge the defects of our experience and reason, not defend them at the expense of what God says.

That then is what people say about the authority of the Bible. But what does the Bible itself tell us about its authority?

2. Where Authority Comes From

There is no one greater than God Himself, and therefore all authority belongs to Him. See how Jesus expressed this in Matthew 28:18:

"... *All authority* .... in heaven and earth has been given *to me* .... "

- If God gives His word to someone else for them to speak it out, does the message have the same or less authority? Look up Jeremiah 25:3-7 and Luke 1:18-20. Does the message only have as much authority as the speaker has, or does it have the authority of God?

....

- The authority of a message depends not on the status of the speaker but on the status of the one who told him to speak. This is something

26

that we would readily accept in everyday life. If a policeman tells us to move on, we do not question his age and experience in order to assess the weight that lies behind his command; we know that behind this possibly quite young and inexperienced man there is the authority of the Crown. We acknowledge that authority when we obey the constable.

● The authority of Scripture, then, does not depend on the status of its various writers. The Bible's authority comes from its inspiration by God.

A quick test

Do you believe what you read in Genesis because:
a) you believe Moses wrote it?
b) you believe God inspired it?
If you answered (a) you would do well to read through this section again!
If you settled for (b) you have obviously understood so far. Well done!

3. The Authority of the Old Testament

Let's see what evidence we can find in the Bible that shows how we should regard the Old Testament.

A. The prophets

It is taken for granted in the Old Testament that the words of the prophets have God's authority behind them. Look up and complete the following:

Joshua 1:17 — "Be careful to obey all the law ....

.... gave you; do not turn from it to the right or to the left, that you may be successful wherever you go."

1 Kings 2:3 — "Observe what ...the Lord your God...

requires: Walk in his ways, and keep his decrees and commands, his laws and requirements, as written in the Law of ...Moses... "

2 Kings 14:6 — "... the Book of the Law of ...of Moses... where

...the Lord... commanded..."

27

Daniel 9:10 — "We have not obeyed the Lord our God or kept the laws he gave us through *his servants the prophets*."

B. Jesus

Jesus clearly regarded the Old Testament as having authority. It has been calculated that He quoted from twenty-four Old Testament books, referring to Daniel twenty-two times, to Isaiah forty times and to the books of Moses sixty times. However, He never quoted Rabbinical authorities at all, unlike the other teachers of His day who relied heavily on these sources. Obviously, for Him the Old Testament stood head and shoulders above these lesser authorities.

Look up Matthew 15:4 and Matthew 22:31. Words that Moses uttered

are quoted by Jesus as being words spoken by ....

Find Luke 22:37 and John 10:35. What characteristic of Scripture does Jesus refer to here?

....

Look up Matthew 19:4-5, Matthew 12:40-41 and Luke 17:26-32. Jesus refers to four Old Testament stories as being factual. Which are they?

1. .... 2. ....

3. .... 4. ....

C. The apostles

The apostles followed the example of Jesus in making the Old Testament their final authority.

Find Romans 9:17 and Galatians 3:8. In these two passages, instead of

referring to "God", Paul uses the word ....

Now look up Hebrews 1:6-12. God is quoted as saying things that were

in fact written by .... and ....

The apostles were obviously gripped by the idea that all that was foretold in the Old Testament had to be fulfilled, and that they had witnessed this fulfilment in the person and ministry of Jesus of Nazareth. Time and again they root their ministry in the Old Testament prophecies, and appeal to the authority of what was written in order to justify their actions.

You might like to find some of these passages to see for yourself how the apostles regarded the Old Testament: Acts 13:46-48; Romans 1:1-4; 4:1-8; 16:25-27; 2 Corinthians 1:20; 6:16-7:1; Galatians 4:27-31.

We see then that the Old Testament scriptures were not regarded as mere religious writings equal in value to many other works of devotion or teaching. They were used as final authority: to refer to what was written was to end all debate. There was no thought of making allowances for scientific ignorance on the part of the writers, nor for any other weaknesses, for these words are God's words.

4. The Authority of the New Testament

The authority of the New Testament depends on two things: the authority of the Lord Jesus and the special commission given by Him to the original apostles.

A. Jesus taught with authority

Although both Jesus and His disciples appealed frequently to the authority of the Old Testament in order to prove that what they were saying and doing was in line with God's Word, we can also see that Jesus felt able to teach on the basis of His own authority. What was it that so amazed His hearers? Turn to Matthew 7:28-29.

"Because He taught as ....

....

The teachers of the Law derived their authority to make pronouncements from the learned judgements passed down by their predecessors. Jesus, however, quoted none of these authorities. He dared to speak using only the authority of Scripture and His own words. He would say things like, "You have been taught such and such, but *I* tell you ..." No wonder the crowds were amazed! They were not used to hearing people who dared to bring their own teaching — everybody was normally busily quoting everybody else!

What gave Jesus the right to speak like this? You will find the answer in John 8:38a:

"I am telling you ....

....

In a very special way, Jesus' words were words from God. That was why He claimed that though heaven and earth were to pass away,

".." (Mark 13:31).

B.   Jesus gave his disciples authority
● Two reasons were in Jesus' mind when He chose the twelve disciples. Found in Mark 3:14, these two reasons were:

   1. "that they might ...." and

   2. "that he might ...."
   What they went out to preach came from what they saw and heard while they were with Him.
● The Holy Spirit was promised to them to enable them to teach accurately what they had themselves been taught by Jesus. Look up and complete the following verses:
   John 14:26 — "But the Counsellor, the Holy Spirit ... will teach you

   all things and will ....

   ...."

   John 16:15b — "... the Spirit will ....

   ...."
● The diet of the early church was the apostles' teaching (Acts 2:42). This body of teaching, together with the Old Testament, was the yardstick for judging what was truth and what was error.
   Look up and complete the following verses, noting the key words:

   Romans 6:17 — "... you wholeheartedly ....

   .... entrusted."

1 Corinthians 11:2 — "I praise you for ... holding to ....
.... on to you."

2 Thessalonians 2:15 — "... stand firm and hold to ....
....
.... or by letter."

Jude 3 — "... contend for ....
.... to the saints."

It is clear from looking at just these verses that the teaching of the apostles was not only delivered in spoken messages but also written down and sent to the churches. Equally, accounts of the ministry of Jesus were written down as time went on, giving the church two sources of written authority: the Old Testament and the apostolic writings. Both these were regarded by them as "Scripture", as we have seen from 2 Peter 3:15-16.

Just as the writers of the books we call the Old Testament wrote what God was breathing out, so the New Testament books were produced by the same miraculous process. Jesus came in order to be God speaking to us (see Hebrews 1:2) and His Spirit was given so that His disciples could accurately recall and teach what He had taught. Our New Testament has the same authority that Jesus has — and He is God!

5. What This Authority Means in Practice

Because we recognise the supreme authority of God, His words are our final authority in everything. This is not a belief to which we pay lip-service while continuing to do things our way. We remember what Jesus said about those who listen to His words but fail to obey what He says. (The story is in Matthew 7:24-27.) We must be people whose lives are a living illustration of what God has said — for God's Word is for living!

Traditions must change. We cannot say that the traditions of the church are as important as the Bible. Traditions have a habit of crowding God's word out of our thinking, so that we are happy to follow the customary

31

way of doing things with no thought of checking to see if we are doing things God's way (see Mark 7:1-13).

Those who see in the traditional teachings of the church a source of authority are immediately faced with a problem: different branches of the church have different and often conflicting traditions. On what basis do we decide which to follow? Where is our final authority?

Further, we see that these traditions have arisen, at best, in response to what was believed to be the leading of the Holy Spirit. As we know from our own experience, this response is always imperfect. The Bible, on the other hand, is not an imperfect response to the prompting of the Spirit — it has been breathed out by God Himself. The Bible then is our final authority by which we judge and test the varying traditions of the churches.

Experience is unreliable. Often we set aside what the Bible says for reasons like:

"I tried that once, but it didn't work!"

"No one has ever seen that happen!"

"If none of the great saints ever experienced that, then it can't be necessary!"

All these arguments are using human experience as the final authority. However, our experience is just that: human. The Bible, on the other hand, is divine, and must be allowed to pass judgement on our defective experience.

Intellect must yield. We have no right to assume arrogantly that we of the twentieth century can spot the flaws in God's thinking! The Bible was breathed out by God. Our proper response is to humble ourselves as we read it. The fact is that even if all the leading academics of this world combined to assert that the Bible is false, our position would not be changed: "Let God be true, and every man a liar." (Romans 3:4) We must never be tricked into trying to fit the Bible into science, as if science were fact and the Bible open to question. God *knows* the truth; the scientist is merely trying, within his limitations, to *discover* it.

We prophesy in part. The gift of prophecy is a wonderful and vital gift. However, the prophet is not speaking a "God-breathed" word. He is merely trying to express truth that the Spirit of God has brought to him. His expression of that truth might well leave room for improvement. Prophecy must always be judged (1 Cor 14:29). Scripture can be used in order to do this. Scripture is truth; "prophecy" might not be.

Obey now! We do not need to wait for a "now" word before we obey God. God HAS spoken, and the words written down are there to be obeyed. Paul, in Ephesians 4:28, tells the person who has been stealing to stop doing so. He does not say, "If you have had a theft problem you really need God to speak to you about it!"

Obviously there will be times when particular words in the Bible will come to us with a special force. But we are not to assume that unless this happens we can disregard what God has said.

What did Jesus say we must obey? Turn to Matt 28:20:

"...teaching them to obey ....
I have commanded you."

He did not say that we should be taught to obey everything that comes to us as a "living" word. Nowhere does the Bible distinguish between the Word of God in general and the word that comes with special relevance. It is ALL the Word of God.

As we saw at the beginning of this chapter, there are those who have developed a doctrine about *rhema* words. They use the fact that there are two Greek words for "word" (*rhema* and *logos*) to make a distinction between a dynamic "now" word and the static written word. This idea is expressed in different ways by different teachers, but most forms of it display a disturbing tendency almost to devalue the Bible as it stands. What matters is to have a *rhema*: a verse of scripture that excites an inner response of faith.

The simple fact is that there are indeed two different Greek words for "word" in the New Testament, but they are interchangeable and have no identifiable difference of meaning. For example, Matthew 12:36 says that "men will have to give account on the day of judgement for every careless word they have spoken." The word used here for "word" is *rhema*. But then v.37 continues the theme but switches to the word *logos*. "For by your words you will be acquitted, and by your words you will be condemned." Can anyone seriously claim that the meaning changes from v.36 to v.37? Surely not.

So we do not believe that the Bible merely contains words that can come alive and become God's Word to us; the Bible IS God's Word to us.

Enough said. Right at the beginning, the apostles had to warn against those who were adding to what God had said (see Colossians 2:8, for example). God is not going to add to the Scriptures in any way, and no other teachings can aspire to the authority that the Bible has. Look up the following verses and answer the questions:

2 Timothy 3:17 — Does the Bible partially equip us or completely equip us?

....

Jude 3 — Has the faith been partly revealed to us or once for all given to us?

....

Obviously the Bible does not tell us all we need to know about everything — it's a little weak on car maintenance for example! — but it does tell us all we need to know if we are to come to maturity as the people of God. Beware the teaching or prophetic utterance or "sense of God's leading" that does not fit with what God has said in the Bible. The Bible has final authority to judge everything else.

Satan knows it! Because the Bible has authority, it is a very effective weapon to use against the Devil. Paul calls it a "sword" (Eph 6:17), while the Gospels show us how Jesus used it as that (Matt 4:4,7,10).

Flaunt it! We must not be defensive or apologetic about what the Bible says. It carries far more weight than our opinions and arguments. Our preaching, witnessing, praying etc. should be full of what God has said. We are not ashamed of it; we delight in it!

None of this means that we have to close our eyes to difficulties that we find in the Bible. In our next lesson we will see how to handle these.

Lesson 4 FACING UP TO DIFFICULTIES

It is very important that our minds should be convinced of the truth of the Scriptures. Certainly it is by faith that we accept the Bible as the Word of God, but there should be no difference between what we believe and what we think. Christians who never use their minds are unlikely to come to maturity! If you believe things without ever really thinking about them, you could well come to grief when you meet opposition that is plausible and apparently based on hard evidence. So, we do not ignore difficulties, we face up to them and look for answers. Of course, that is not the same as saying that we should refuse to believe the Bible until all our questions or doubts have been convincingly answered! All we are saying is that faith is not blind. If something is true, then it will be seen to be true; it will stand closer examination.

1. Let's Get It Straight

As we have seen so far in this course, the Bible is truth that has been revealed by God, and written down as He breathed it out. It therefore has His authority. Our reason or ability to accept something is not our final authority: the Bible is.

We are not to sit arrogantly in judgement on what God says, for He tells

us that He esteems the one who ".. my word." (Isaiah 66:2b)

Because the Bible is "God-breathed", it comes from a realm that is above ours. God is greater than us, and His wisdom is far greater than our wisdom. We must realise that, as we think about difficulties in the Bible, *our viewpoint is very restricted*. If we knew everything as God does, then many of these apparent problems would be swept away.

35

Look up and complete:

1 Corinthians 1:25 — "For the foolishness of God is ....

.... "

Isaiah 55:8-9 — " 'For my thoughts are not your thoughts, neither are your ways my ways,' declares the Lord. 'As the heavens are higher than the earth,

so are my ways .... your ways and my thoughts than your thoughts.' "

(NOTE: Paul is not suggesting that God is ever "foolish". It is as if he were saying: "Even if God *were* foolish, His foolishness would be far wiser than our wisdom could ever be!")

Science is NOT God! The pronouncement of a scientist should never be regarded as the last word on the subject; further discovery and research will inevitably change the situation. It would be foolish to reject what God has said simply because a particular branch of science has not yet advanced far enough to agree with the Biblical revelation!

We need to bear these points in mind, then, as we begin to look at some of the areas where we might have difficulties. And let's keep a right sense of proportion — the Bible is not all problems! As Mark Twain is quoted as saying: "It's not the things I don't understand in the Bible that bother me; it's the things I do understand!"

2.   Going Round in Circles

A problem that some people have is in the way we have tried to establish the authority of the Bible. "Surely it's not right," they say, "to argue for the authority of the Bible by quoting the Bible. You are going round in circles!"

It's certainly a good point — at least, it is until you think more deeply about it. You see, if we believe that the Bible is our final authority, then we cannot appeal to any higher authority to back up our belief. Were we to do so, then THAT would be our final authority.

It would be like the man who said, "My wife says I am to be the head in our home!" That statement shows that he is not really the boss: his wife is!

Because the Bible is our final authority, we have to let it speak for itself. When we do that, we discover that it has authority in our lives. As Jesus reminded His disciples:

"The words I have spoken to you are .... and they are

............................" (John 6:63)

3. But Science Tells Us ...

Perhaps the major problem that we meet as we study the Bible is the apparent conflict between what we read there and current scientific thought.

For example, one could draw the conclusion from the Bible that:
- the earth is supported by foundations (1 Sam 2:8)
- it rains when gates are opened in heaven (Gen 7:11)
- the earth does not move (Psalm 93:1)

Furthermore, thinking now about how we are made, we could be led to believe, if we use an older version of the Bible, that:
- our kidneys (reins) have a teaching function (Psalm 16:7 AV)
- our bones are able to speak (Psalm 35:10 AV)
- our bowels produce mercy (Colossians 3:12 AV)

(NOTE: The modern translations express the sense in a less startling way!)

If we are going to be fair, we would have to admit that these references are really in the same sort of category as many of the expressions that we use today, like:
- "the four corners of the earth"
- "sunrise" and "sunset"
- "I felt in my bones that that would happen"
- "a gut reaction"

Obviously, none of these expressions are intended to reflect our scientific beliefs, any more than the Bible references we have looked at can be taken as scientific statements.

On a much more important level is the whole issue of "evolution versus Genesis". Many learned books have been published on this subject, and this is not the place to attempt a dazzlingly convincing solution. However, there are some basic guiding principles that we can point to:
- It is a symptom of godlessness to put created things in the place of the Creator. Godless man prefers to find his origin in a natural process

of "things" evolving rather than in the loving purpose of the God he wants to ignore. Look up Romans 1:21-25 to see how Paul teaches this, and then read the verses that follow this passage to see what happens to a society that chooses to think like this.

- An honest scientist will only state what has been proved. He considers the material evidence and draws reasonable conclusions. He can only study the *results* of God's creating work; he was not there to witness it taking place and therefore he can have nothing to say about it. Look up Job 38:4. God is in a far better position to tell us how things happened than any mere man can be, isn't He!

- Scientific investigation is never complete. The beliefs of one generation of scientists will be regarded as primitive by their successors. We would be foolish to entertain doubts about the Bible on the strength of current scientific opinion — those opinions will certainly change. Indeed, we can be quite sure that true science must eventually agree with the Bible — since God is the Author both of the Bible and the evidence that the scientists investigate.

4. What Really Happened?

Have you ever been confused by some of the vast numbers mentioned in the Bible, or by the apparently conflicting accounts of the same story given in different places? Is this evidence that the Bible is unreliable?

Those numbers. John Wenham, in *The Lion Handbook to the Bible*, has pointed out that the impossibly large numbers that we find in the Bible do not, in fact, show the Bible to be unreliable. The vastness of the numbers points to a simpler explanation than the often-heard one that it has all been made up. "Would any man in his senses," he asks, "invent a story of a bus crash in which 16,000 passengers were killed?"

The problem stems from Hebrew. For many years, Hebrew was written using just consonants; the reader had to supply the vowels himself. A problem arose with the word for "thousand"; minus its vowels, it was identical to the word for the captain of a thousand. Just to complicate things, the word for "thousand" is also used to mean a family or clan.

So we can see that some of those impossible numbers can be cut down to a more realistic size, not by tampering with the text, but by allowing for the wrong translation of identical words.

Hebrew numbers can vary alarmingly with the stroke of a pen. As the Old Testament was copied by hand for many generations, it is not difficult to accept that figures could be wrongly copied.

Look up 2 Samuel 10:18 and 1 Chronicles 19:18. An apparent contradiction in the numbers involved can simply be explained as an error of copying.

What happened when. Those who were used to write this wonderful book were more concerned with the *meaning* of the things they were recording than the *exact order* of events. We must not expect to find the same concept of reporting in the Bible that we hope for in our newspapers.

As we study the Bible and attempt to piece together some sort of time-scale, there are some important things to bear in mind.

a. Names that seem to refer to a person can also refer to the tribe coming from that person. So "Israel" can be the man of that name, or the tribe descending from him. Thus, when we look through a list of "so-and-so begat so-and-so", and try, roughly, to add up the years represented by it, we can be quite wrong: some of the names could stand for tribes that descended from other tribes.

b. "Son of" can mean "descendant of". So, in Matthew 1:1, when we read that Jesus Christ was "the son of David, the son of Abraham", we are not to assume that Abraham was the grandfather of Jesus. He wasn't! There were many other generations between the two.

c. Years are not to be understood in terms of our calendar. They could be reckoned by the moon, the agricultural seasons or the reign of the king.

d. No writer is under an obligation to record everything about his subject. Did John tell us everything about Jesus, or just as much as he needed to prove his point? See John 21:25.

   If the writers selected material, then their differing versions must not be seen as contradicting each other, but as amplifying each other.

   Look up Matthew 27:37, Mark 15:26, Luke 23:38 and John 19:19. Now write what you think was actually written on the cross:

....

e. The writers were free to present their material in the way that would be easiest for their intended readers to understand. So, Luke, writing for Gentiles, says that the crowd shouted, "Glory in the highest!" where the other Gospels have "Hosanna in the highest!". All he is doing is giving the sense, so that the non-Jew could understand it.

5. That's Not Loving!

There are many things in the Bible that strike us as being unacceptably harsh. How can we come to terms with these things? Can the God who instructed His people to do such things really be the God whom we know to be full of love?

For example, in Deuteronomy 7:2, Israel is told that when they have defeated the nations living in the Promised Land, they are to "destroy them totally" and "show them no mercy". As if that were not enough, in verse 16 they are told:

"You must ....
.... gives over

to you. Do not ....
and do not serve their gods, for that will be a snare to you."

We need to remember that sin always needs drastic treatment. The God who gave these awful commands to Israel is the God we see dealing with His Son at Calvary. Sin has a dreadful penalty.

If one nation is to be victorious, then another has to be defeated. If one is delivered it is because the oppressor is judged. And it follows that the more complete the victory, the more total will be the defeat of the other side. This is gloriously true with regard to our salvation. It is also true, in the Old Testament, of the deliverance that God brought time and again to Israel.

6. Surprising Quotes

Sometimes, when the New Testament writers quote the Old Testament, you may get the impression that they had rather bad memories — the quotes are not very accurate. For example, look up Matthew 12:18-21 and compare it with Isaiah 42:1-4. There's quite a difference, isn't there?

There is, in fact, a simple reason for this. Some two hundred years before Jesus came, a Greek translation of the Old Testament had been made in North Africa. As the New Testament writers were writing in Greek, when they wanted to use an Old Testament quotation they generally used this Greek version. So, as we read what they wrote, we are reading an English translation of a Greek translation of the Hebrew original. Then, as we turn to the Old Testament, we read an English translation straight from the original Hebrew. What has come by the direct route is likely to differ from what has come by a more roundabout route.

In some cases, the difference in the quotation has another cause. The writers are not in fact quoting a text, they are reinterpreting it, under the inspiration of the Holy Spirit. An example of this can be found by comparing Ephesians 4:8b with Psalm 68:18:

Ephesians 4:8b — "... he led captives in his train and ....

gifts .... men."

Psalm 68:18 — "... you led captives in your train; you ....

gifts .... men."

The picture is of a victorious king returning home. He takes the spoil of battle and shares it with his men. The Psalm refers to the taking of spoil, while Ephesians speaks of what is done with the spoil: it is given to men. So you see, this is not a misquotation, but an example of the Holy Spirit bringing out the meaning of what was originally written.

There are a few other quotations in the Bible which can cause raised eyebrows: these are quotations from works that are not inspired by God. This can give rise to the thought that maybe the writers believed they were quoting God's Word; maybe something has been left out of the Bible that should be there!

Really they were only doing what a preacher might do today. In the course of his message, he will quote from the Bible, but he might also quote some verses from a hymn, or even, say, from Shakespeare (if he is a really well-educated preacher!). No one would conclude that this preacher put hymns and Shakespeare on the same level as Scripture — I hope!

So, Paul quoted "some of your own poets" when he was preaching to the crowd in Athens (see Acts 17:28). He quotes a saying from Menander to the Corinthians (see 1 Corinthians 15:33). Jude, on the other hand, causes some people all sorts of problems by referring to, and quoting, two apocryphal works (see Jude 9,14).

While the works being quoted are not inspired by God, the quotations in their Biblical settings are inspired by God, and this is what really matters.

7. What About Miracles?

We are not suggesting that the miracles recorded in the Bible represent a problem to us — they do not. The problem lies not in the miracles themselves but in the modern approach to them. For example, it is normal for young people to be taught in school that they should not be regarded as miracles at all. The argument runs like this: miracles do not happen, therefore the events presented as miracles in the Bible were not really miracles at all — they must have a natural explanation. Thus, we are told, when the Bible speaks of Jesus walking on the water, what really happened was that the disciples were so terrified by the storm that they failed to notice that they were almost at the shore. So, when they saw Jesus coming towards them through the shallow water, they assumed He was walking on top of the water. Thus there was no miracle at all!

How do we handle this sort of approach? Basically we have to ask ourselves two simple questions: Do we believe in God? Who do we believe God is?

If we believe in the God who has revealed Himself in the Scriptures, we believe in a mighty God who has created everything that exists for His own pleasure and glory. And if God made everything by His own power, then we can share Jeremiah's confidence in Jeremiah 32:17 that "nothing is

...."

It is inevitable that the God who made the heavens will not be limited to working within the bounds of what is possible for us. He is, after all, God!

We need to understand that those who deny the possibility of miracles are really confessing that they do not know the living God. If we know Him, we know something of His power.

As we have seen, we need to be aware of difficulties and be willing to think them through realistically and humbly. But we must not exaggerate them as some do who pronounce the Bible to be full of contradictions. It isn't! On the contrary, it is remarkable that a book written over such a long period by so many different people could have such a high degree of harmony in what it teaches. On this evidence alone, we would have to draw the conclusion that there must be something unusual, not to say supernatural, about its origin.

But, if it was written by so many people over a long time, how did it all get put together? Who decided what should be included, and how do we know that they got it right? We look at these things in our next lesson.

We have seen a number of important things so far:

● God has revealed Himself to us in words.

● Those words were 'breathed out' by specially chosen men.

● Because they come from God, those words have His authority.

But a question still remains to be answered: how can we be sure that the book that we know today as the Bible is exactly the same as that which God inspired thousands of years ago?

While we are happy to accept that the words originally written down were nothing less than God's words, if, at some stage, some sort of council or committee had to decide what was Scripture and what was not, then there is a weak link in the chain: men can make mistakes.

How, then, was the list of Scripture drawn up — and by whose authority was it done? (Incidentally, the technical term for this list is the "canon" of Scripture. "Canon" comes from a Greek word meaning a rod or a carpenter's rule. So the "canon" refers to those books which have been "measured" and judged to be the Word of God.)

1.   Putting the Old Testament Together

We have to admit that very little is known about the development of the Old Testament, although there are one or two facts that can be pieced together.

A.   What's in it

In the Hebrew Bible the Old Testament is divided into three sections:

1. First there is the **Law**. This consists of the five books of Moses: Genesis, Exodus, Leviticus, Numbers and Deuteronomy.

2. Then there is the section known as the **Prophets**. These are divided into the Former Prophets — Joshua, Judges, Samuel and Kings, and the Latter Prophets — Isaiah, Jeremiah, Ezekiel, Hosea, Joel, Amos, Obadiah, Jonah, Micah, Nahum, Habakkuk, Zephaniah, Haggai, Zechariah and Malachi.
3. Finally there are the **Writings**. Here we find Psalms, Proverbs, Job, Ruth, Song of Songs, Ecclesiastes, Lamentations, Esther, Daniel, Ezra, Nehemiah and Chronicles.

So, in Luke 11:51 (look it up!), Jesus is referring to the whole Old Testament period when He mentions these two events, for one is found in Genesis (4:8), and the other in the last book in the Hebrew Scriptures, 2 Chronicles (24:20-21).

B. How it developed

We can see from the Old Testament itself that the Law was received as God's word from an early stage. Certainly by the time of Ezra we find the nation rising as one man to show their assent to this book. The account of this event is found in Nehemiah 8:1-5.

Next, it is thought that the prophetic writings were added to the Book of the Law. This was possibly as a reaction against the spread of Greek culture: it became necessary to hear the words of the prophets and keep them safe lest the essential distinctiveness of the people of God should be lost.

Finally, the other writings that did not fall into either of the previous categories were generally accepted as having authority from God.

But you might still be wondering who made these important decisions. The simple answer is that there is no evidence of the matter ever being discussed in the Old Testament period. Why do you think that is?

Find John 10:3-5. Why do the sheep follow the shepherd?

"Because they ...."

On the other hand, they run away from strangers,

"Because they ....

...."

46

The Scriptures did not need to be debated by learned men simply because there was nothing to debate. God's people recognised God's voice.

Another factor that can help us to be sure of the Old Testament is the attitude of Jesus to it. Remember that Jesus came into the world as the Word of God made flesh. He said of himself:

"... the truth." (John 14:6)

One would expect that, had the Jews been accepting something as Scripture that was not Scripture, or if they were overlooking something that was genuinely from God but had never gained acceptance, He would have corrected them. But He never raised the matter.

If Jesus accepted the Old Testament without hesitation, then so can we. Obviously, God not only spoke to His people, He also took care to see that what He said was preserved and accepted.

C. Changing the order

In the previous lesson we referred to a Greek translation of the Old Testament that was circulated in North Africa. In fact, this translation, known as the Septuagint, was more a book of Jewish literature than a translation of the Old Testament, as it included several other devotional works as well as the Scriptures. What matters for our purposes is that it also altered the order of the Old Testament books from that of the Hebrew Bible. Subsequently, when a Latin translation of the Bible was made, the Old Testament was translated from this Greek version, retaining the new order and even including some of the additional books, which have become known as the "Apocrypha".

As these extra books were never accepted by the Jews as Scripture, Protestants have been united in rejecting them, although Catholics have retained them. However, the order taken over from the Septuagint has stuck, and so it is that order that we have in our Bibles today.

2. Putting the New Testament Together

Because it happened in more recent times, we have a much clearer view of how the New Testament came into being. Let's see what happened.

A. The early church

The first Christians looked to three sources for the teaching that formed the basis of their lives:

(i) First, they followed the example that Jesus had set them and made the Old Testament scriptures their authority. If you study the sermons that are recorded in the Book of Acts you will see how heavily they relied on the Old Testament. See Acts 2:14-39; 3:12-26; 4:8-12; 7:2-53, etc.

(ii) Then they had accounts of the life and teaching of Jesus. At first these were carefully passed on by word of mouth — a thing that might amaze us, if we have problems trying to memorise one or two verses! In fact, people who are not used to reading and writing often have far better memories than those who have become used to writing things down. However, as the generation that had been eyewitnesses of Jesus' ministry began to die out, these accounts were written down, becoming the "Gospels" in our New Testament. Look up Acts 10:37-38 for an example of how the story of Jesus was passed on.

(iii) The third source of instruction for the early church was in the letters circulated by the apostles. At an early stage these were regarded as Scripture by the church — this is the clear implication of 2 Peter 3:15-16.

B. After the apostles

As time went on, various devotional books began to achieve popularity amongst Christians. These books made no claim to be inspired, but confusion could easily arise for some people. You see, many of these works were what we would call "historical romances". They were fiction, but they used the names of actual people — in many cases the apostles tended to have a starring role.

It was necessary to define what was inspired and what was not. Unfortunately, the first to produce such a list was himself not exactly reliable. Marcion had some rather odd beliefs about there being two gods in conflict with each other. He produced a list of books that he considered safe for his followers. Needless to say, it was not a very full list!

The need was now even greater that people should be protected from what was fanciful, and lists began to appear stating what was apostolic and what was not.

There was no question of the Church deciding what was Scripture; it was more a matter of declaring what was generally accepted among the churches as a defence against false teachers. Those books were accepted which were true to the teaching of the apostles and showed evidence of having been written or supervised by the apostles. By the close of the fourth century controversy had died down and none has arisen since.

We are confident that the Bible we have is given by God. The Church did not create it — rather, the Church has agreed that this book is the authentic voice of the God we know, and this conviction is confirmed by the Holy Spirit.

3. As Originally Given?

Obviously many hundreds of years passed from the time the canon of Scripture was completed until the invention of the printing press. During those centuries the Bible had to be painstakingly copied by hand. If you can imagine settling down to a task like that, I imagine that you would reckon on making one or two mistakes before you were through!

The original manuscripts have long since disappeared. All we have are fragments of manuscripts of different parts of the Bible. These do not always agree with each other — due to errors in copying — and so scholars have to decide what is likely to have been the original wording. This is why modern translations have footnotes that give alternatives to the printed text.

Lest you should think that we can't be sure of ANY of the Bible, let us quickly say that the vast bulk of the Bible is not affected by any variations in the various manuscripts. And where there are doubts, no major truth is at stake. God did not reveal His Word and then leave us to spoil it and lose parts of it; He has surely watched over it so that all generations can hear it.

Amongst all the copying and translating of Scripture, a vital change was introduced in the twelfth and sixteenth centuries. In the twelfth century the Bible was divided into chapters, while in the sixteenth century it was further divided into verses. While this is very helpful if you want to find a particular passage (imagine trying to write a book like this without being able to refer to verses in the Bible!), one has to admit that these divisions were NOT inspired by God and can sometimes break up a passage in an unfortunate way. Be on your guard!

The Bible we use today, in whatever version we read it, is not exactly the same as it was when it flowed from the pens of its writers. The language and form have changed; the truth expressed, however, is the same. God has spoken to man. The Bible is God's Word. In our next lesson we shall consider the implications of this truth.

Consistently through the Bible we find that truth is taught to create a response. There is always a "therefore". What response should we give to the things we have learned in this course so far?

First, let's summarise what we have seen:

- God has revealed Himself to men. Particularly, He has revealed His purpose to save people through Christ in words spoken through people.
- These words were faithfully spoken out and written down as a result of a supernatural work of God.
- What God has spoken has His authority. This takes precedence over all other sources of authority.
- From our position of limited knowledge and understanding, we find some things in the Bible difficult to accept. We can be quite sure, however, that if our understanding were not so restricted, these difficulties would fade away.
- Those who have been "born of God" recognise His voice. The nature of God's Word has ensured its complete acceptance from the time it was first given.

What should be our response to these facts? One thing is clear: we should not merely try to memorise these matters so that we can claim to have learned "the doctrine of Scripture"! No, we need to spend time thinking about the implications of these truths.

1. Our Doctrine is the Scripture

We must not fall into the trap of paying lip-service to the authority of Scripture while placing a greater reliance on the traditions within which we have been reared. This was the fault for which Jesus criticised the Pharisees and teachers of the Law.

Look at Mark 7:8-13. In verse 8 He says: "You have let go of ....

.... and are holding on to

.... "

The effect of this attitude is shown by verse 13: "You ....
the word of God by your tradition that you have handed down."

What we believe is determined by the clear teaching of Scripture, NOT by:
- the restraints imposed by particular systems of doctrine. We do not, for example, conform to Calvinism or Arminianism — but to Scripture. (Of course, we cannot prevent people attaching labels to us, but we are responsible for ensuring that we are true to the Word of God rather than the systems of men, no matter how godly those men might be.)
- the traditions of our denomination.
- the opinion of the majority.
- the trends current in the world around us.

Jesus warned of the awful possibility of even those chosen by God being deceived in the last days. Read what He said in Matthew 24:24. We need to check everything by what God has said if we are to be safe.

2. Our Message is the Scripture

We do not need to apologise for what the Bible says, nor should it have a minor role while the focus is on *our* opinions and experiences. It is God's Word that has authority, and therefore it should dominate our preaching and teaching and be at the centre of our witnessing.

Have you noticed how so many of the things we introduce to back up the presentation of the truth have a habit of taking over and pushing the Bible into the background? This can happen with drama, music, visual aids of all kinds, etc.

The Bible is our message ...
- ... when the church gathers together. Look at 1 Timothy 4:13, where

  Paul refers to three vital matters: ....

  ...., ...

  and ....

52

- ... in our evangelism. Look at 2 Corinthians 4:2, where Paul speaks of his refusal to distort God's Word. On the contrary, his method is to set "... plainly."
- ... in our everyday witnessing. In Philippians 2:16, Paul tells the believers how to express the reality of salvation in their lives. This new way of living is to be the setting in which they "hold out ....

...."
- ... as we instruct our children. This was the pattern in Israel, as we see from Deuteronomy 6:7. In 2 Timothy 3:15 we have a glimpse of how this had been a significant part of Timothy's upbringing.
- ... in spiritual warfare. God's Word has an authority that the powers of Hell have to recognise. This is why the word of God is singled out as THE weapon for spiritual warfare in Ephesians 6:17.

3. Our Methods Come from the Scripture

Jesus taught that the new life that the Spirit brings cannot be contained in an inflexible system (see Matthew 9:16-17). Those of us who have been Christians for any length of time will have discovered how easily we accept ways of doing things without questioning them. We then find ourselves trying to fit what the Bible says into our inflexible container. It doesn't work.

If we believe that the Bible has authority, we will not tamper with it to make it fit our methods. We will scrap our methods, no matter how much we have come to cherish them, and obey God.

- We will examine our pattern of church activities and ask whether they are the best way of expressing the church life that the Bible teaches.
- We will take a hard look at the structure of our services and ask whether they allow the gifts and ministries that God has put in the Body to be expressed in a Biblical way.
- We will note what the New Testament says about baptism and the Lord's Table and ensure that our own practice conforms to this.
- We will be willing to change the pattern of leadership in the church from one that expresses career or status to one that is based on gift.

It is when we touch sensitive and controversial areas like these that we see whether or not we really base our lives on the authority of the Word of God. The possibility can be that we *say* that we believe in the authority of Scripture while *in practice* we are bound by the power of tradition. Indeed, to obey God can seem a very risky course to take; to be out of step with accepted norms makes you vulnerable to criticism, misunderstanding and even opposition. But of course, we are following a Saviour who chose just such a path.

QUESTION: Do your church's methods and structures reflect the power of tradition, expediency or the Word of God?

4. Our Thinking is Shaped by Scripture

All of us have absorbed attitudes and opinions from the people who have been around us for as long as we have been aware. If we are to experience what God has for us, those attitudes and opinions will need to be corrected — by the Bible.

Our upbringing may have left us with a view of ourselves that is damaging and restricting. We may feel that we are bound to fail no matter how hard we try. We may even doubt that God really loves us. What we need to do, James tells us in chapter one, verses 22-25 of his letter, is to take a good hard look at ourselves in the "mirror" of God's Word, remember what we see there, and live as the person we see there: a child of God, loved, forgiven and empowered by Him.

What is it that Paul says will have the effect of transforming us? Look up Romans 12:2 and write it out here:

"...

....

....

...."

This verse tells us that we can be pressured by **the world around us** into conforming to its pattern, or we can be transformed from the inside out. Such a transformation can only take place when our minds are gripped by what God says. If only we would think the truth, we would come into God's purposes for us much more easily.

54

As our minds are taught by Scripture we will no longer be the product of our past or of our environment, and we will increasingly be recognisable as the children of God. But a vital part of this transformation is our recognition of the extent to which we have been influenced by the world around us, and in particular by the media and the opinions of our circle of friends. We have probably absorbed a whole framework of attitudes and beliefs that have little in common with the mind of God. Too many amongst us are Christian in name but humanist in outlook! We must acknowledge that prevailing opinions are not usually pleasing to God. Look up and complete Romans 8:7:

"The sinful mind is .... to God."

You may find it helpful to list some of the issues that people feel strongly about at the moment. Now, how did you form your own opinions about these things? Did you BEGIN by looking to see what the Bible has to say? Where did you get your beliefs from about marriage and divorce, abortion, raising children, the role of women, politics, etc.?

We demonstrate our belief in the authority of Scripture by thinking Biblically on every issue.

If you find that your mind resists what you read in the Bible, don't just ignore the problem, but speak with the leader who is taking you through this course about it. You can be helped.

5. Our Lives Express the Scripture

As you read the Bible, you will become aware that it is not all about "spiritual" things. It is very practical.

The Bible tells us how we can be saved. This salvation involves a new birth (John 3:3), a birth that is the result of the Spirit of God bringing us into new life. From the moment that we are "born again" we have God's life in us. This life is like a "seed" (1 John 3:9) that grows and expresses God's character through our behaviour.

However, we are not automatically holy. This new life needs to be encouraged and directed; that is why there is so much practical instruction in the New Testament. It is not telling us what we "ought" to do; it is telling us what we CAN do, now we are new people, with all the resources of God's grace given to us.

Read quickly through Ephesians 4:25-6:9, and see the everyday things that are spoken of. Note them down:

....

....

....

....

....

....

If we accept that the Bible has authority, then there is no area of our living that will not be affected as we gladly change our behaviour in private, at home, at work, etc. to express the ways of God.

Look up 2 Corinthians 3:2-3. What does Paul say of these believers?

(verse 3) — "You are a ....

....

....

.... "

In other words, if we acknowledge the authority of Scripture in our behaviour, people who watch us will be, as it were, reading a letter from Christ.

In the Bible God has spoken. The Bible is therefore uniquely trustworthy. When God speaks, things happen. We are sure that God has spoken to us and so we devote ourselves to reading what He has said. We come to the Bible with reverence, asking that the same Holy Spirit who was at work in those who wrote it will also work in us to enable us to understand and profit from it.

We not only want to know what God has said, and be built up by the truth, we want to obey Him. As we obey His Word with faith, something wonderful is happening to the world: a company of people is rising who show by their lives that they are sons of God. All of creation (Romans 8:19) is waiting for such a time! In the excitement of this growth, however, we must be careful not to be carried away. We shall reflect on this danger in the next lesson.

Have you ever been unexpectedly overtaken by thick fog as you were going along a familiar road? If so, you will remember having to strain to find landmarks through the fog so that you could stay on course. If you failed to do this, but just kept your eyes on the way ahead, you probably got lost.

In many ways all the new life surging through the church can be like a sudden fog. We can be so aware of all the new things that are happening that we lose sight of the landmarks that would keep us from going off course. In particular there is a danger that the clear teaching of Scripture can be overlooked — overtaken by a host of more contemporary questions and challenges.

In fact, in a time of change, the Bible is more than ever essential reading.

An Important Principle

Jesus once made a comment that is important for what we are looking at in this lesson. You will find it in Matthew 13:52. Have you looked it up and read it? Good! Jesus speaks of a "teacher of the law", that is to say someone who was steeped in the truths that had been passed down through the generations in Israel, being "instructed about the kingdom of heaven". In other words, Jesus is talking about someone who has been brought up in old traditions but who is now learning a lot of revolutionary new truth. What does Jesus say will happen next?

He will bring "out of his storeroom .... treasures as well as ...."

Clearly, as far as Jesus is concerned, those who accept His teaching will still draw heavily on all the revelation of God from generations past. Indeed, Jesus rooted His message in, and proved it from, the Old Testament. He certainly didn't show any kind of inclination to ignore the Scriptures of

59

the Old Testament in favour of new teaching. Rather, he showed that the Scriptures which had guided the people of God through the ages were still to be the diet for those living in a new day.

In the same way, we too need "new treasures as well as old". We want to be totally involved in what God is doing today while keeping our bearings by feeding on and testing everything by the Scriptures.

But what are some of the things that could so absorb and excite us that we could lose our way?

1. Baptism in the Spirit

There is particular danger for those who have been raised in traditional, rather formal churches. A new experience of the Spirit and the freedom He gives can easily make them lose their bearings. After all, the teaching they received in the past probably never gave them any idea that God had all this to give His children! Indeed, it may even have been a major factor in keeping them away from such blessing for years. So it all gets dismissed as part of the "bad old days". And with it goes much that was good: things like a concern to be carefully Biblical, for example.

Lacking any kind of framework of teaching for their new experience, such people can become tragically vulnerable to any kind of strange doctrine from any group or teacher who seems to be part of this exciting new thing they have come into.

But wait — let's get our bearings. Who gave us the Scriptures? You will find the answer in 2 Peter 1:21:

"Men spoke from .... as they were carried along by

...."

You see, there is no conflict or contrast between the Scriptures and the Spirit, for the Spirit is the very one who gave us the Scriptures in the first place. Furthermore, if you look up Ephesians 5:18-19 and Colossians 3:16 you will find two closely parallel passages. But, while the one speaks of being filled with the Spirit, the other says:

"let the .... dwell in you richly".
Clearly, to be filled with the Spirit and to be filled with the Word of God are regarded as being virtually the same.

Indeed, if we are filled with the Spirit and are using the gifts of the Spirit, it is vital that we should also be full of the Word of God in order to test things, and stay on course. It is surely for this very reason that the Bible gives us straightforward instruction on how to use these gifts in 1 Corinthians 12 and 14.

So, a new experience of the Spirit provides us with an opportunity to draw on resources that are both old and new. Our new freedom is enhanced by a solid background of Bible teaching. But freedom without that background can lead us into all kinds of problems.

2. Apostles and Prophets

As we being to get accustomed to the gifts of the Spirit, we are likely to be able to identify people whom God has gifted in particular ways to help the church. You will find some of them mentioned in Ephesians 4:11. Note them down here:

....

.... and ....

We have been familiar with evangelists, pastors and teachers for centuries, but what about apostles and prophets? You will notice that Ephesians 4:13 shows that their ministry lasts until we all reach unity in the faith and become mature. So we still need them very much.

So far, so good. But again we come up against the danger of the new eclipsing the old. We can make a very proper attempt to receive the authoritative ministry of these men, and, in the process, go overboard on their teaching at the expense of God's Word.

For example, if you are listening to a prophet who is sharing his insight into the purposes of God, as you thrill to the excitement and urgency of his words, are you likely to check it with Scripture? Probably not. Especially if his ministry is accompanied by signs and wonders which you feel confirm the truth of what he is saying.

As such prophetic revelation increases, the thought can even be voiced that we are living in a new day that has gone beyond the Bible.

Not so. Jesus said: "Heaven and earth will pass away, but my words will never pass away" (Mark 13:31). The day will never dawn when we have left God's Word behind.

The early church faced the same dangers. Look how Paul had to rebuke the Galatians in Galatians 1:6: "I am astonished," he says, "that you are so quickly deserting the one who called you ... and are turning to ...

...."

Notice also his awesomely strong warning in verse 8. Never mind apostles and prophets, we mustn't even let angels take us beyond what God has already said!

Let us receive all those whom God has anointed to bless His church. But let us be very clear that the test of any person's ministry remains their submission to what God has said in the Bible. We must beware those who treat it flippantly or ignore it. See Acts 20:28-32 and notice how Paul had to warn the people of his day about such matters, and then look at Acts 17:11 for a brilliant example of how to receive an apostle. What did these people do?

"They .... the message with great .... and

.... the Scriptures every day to ....

.... was true."

3. The Supernatural

It's exhilarating to be where God is working, isn't it? What's even more exciting is the possibility that we "ain't seen nothin' yet!" It is more than probable that what we have seen so far is nothing to what we will be seeing soon.

But how does that affect our attitude to the Bible? In a number of ways:

● Studying or preaching the Bible can seem pretty tame or even irrelevant when it is contrasted with the excitement of signs and wonders. So some will say, "Let's scrap the sermon and make room for God to move!"

But we need to reflect that a "sign" is so called because it points to something: the truth of the words being preached. "Works" without "words" are like a sign pointing nowhere.

Turn to Mark 16:20. What was the purpose of the signs that God did?

They "............................ his ...."

● Supernatural experience can distract us from what the Bible says. After all, who cares about doctrine and practical teaching about our lifestyle when God is using them in powerful ways! Surely you can't tell a wife to submit to her husband if she is being used by God in ways that are beyond her husband's experience? And can you tell children who are seeing angels and getting revelation from God that they must obey their parents?

But just think what the churches of which we read in Acts were experiencing. They saw buildings actually shaking as the Spirit came; angels moved amongst them; the dead were raised, while others dropped dead suddenly; whole cities were impacted by the Gospel. (See Acts 4:31, 5:5, 9:40, 8:8, 12:7 and 19:23-27.)

And it was to just such people that the apostles brought teaching about such matters as home life and relationships, handling money, behaviour at work, etc.

The amazing fact is that you can be used by God in remarkable ways and yet still need to be taught how to live. And this, 2 Timothy 3:16-17 tells us, is the function of the Bible.

● An increasing experience of the power of God brings with it a developing store of "know-how". We learn how to handle different circumstances; techniques begin to develop; principles begin to emerge from the mists of our initial ignorance. And so a body of teaching comes into being that is separate from Scripture but perhaps treated as if it were Scripture.

It is always dangerous to add to the Bible. When people make confident assertions about, for example, healing or deliverance, we do well to ask, "Does the Bible say that?" If it is in the Bible it is true; if it is experience or opinion it may be helpful, but it needs to be tested against God's Word.

4. Contemporary Issues

From the days of the early church until now, Christians have been vulnerable to the pressure to keep in step with trends in the world around them. After all, if you don't keep up to date with current thinking you are old-fashioned. And who wants to be regarded as that?

Some will simply assume that if most people think it, it must be right. To say "Everybody knows that ..." can be a very powerful argument! But, if we think at all Biblically, we will recognise, as we saw in Lesson Six, that the minds of those who don't know Christ are hostile to God. So the majority opinion will carry no weight with us.

Others want to be Biblical but want equally to be regarded as "modern", so they get to work on what the Bible says to try to reinterpret it so that it fits with current ideas. The more dramatic the reinterpretation, the more dazzling it can seem to unwary listeners, and so people are led astray.

Now, let's get our bearings. We believe that the Bible is God's breathed-out Word. And because God is who He is, we can be sure that He has always know about the twentieth century. So when He gave the Bible, He gave a book that would be relevant for today. It was not just for "then"; it is for "now". It is not in need of updating; nor does it need to be adapted to fit modern culture. On the contrary, modern culture is in great need of being adapted to fit the Bible!

Travelling as he did from country to country, and hence from culture to culture, Paul must have experienced the temptation to "adapt" the truth to fit the situation. If he did, he resisted it, as he tells us in 2 Corinthians 4:2. He says:

"We do not use ...., nor do we .... the

.... On the contrary, by

setting forth the truth .... we commend ourselves to every man's conscience in the sight of God."

Elsewhere, he warned that the time would come when people would find the truth inconvenient. In 2 Timothy 4:3-5 he warns that:

"to suit their own desires, they will gather around them a great number

of teachers to say ....

.... They will
turn their ears away from the truth and turn aside to myths."

And what is his very practical advice in v.5?

".. in all situations."

The possibility is that we can be swayed by the high profile of a teacher, or dazzled by his ability in demonstrating that a passage doesn't actually mean what it appears to say, with the result that we all too easily set aside the clear teaching of Scripture. We need to "keep our head" — and in doing so, keep our bearings.

The pressure to conform is notoriously strong. So much so that it can come as quite a relief to hear preachers who can convince us that the Bible agrees with trends in society. We don't have to be out of step or face ridicule after all!

No — let's determine that we will stay with the plain, consistent teaching of Scripture — and stay with a clear conscience towards God.

So ...

There will always be dangers in the new, because the new is invariably also the unknown. But that is no reason to recoil to the safety of the past. We want to move with God because we love Him and want to be where He is. So we need to go forward, keeping our bearings from what the Bible says. If we do this, we will be able to discern truth from error and safely embrace every new thing that God is doing. If we set Scripture aside, we will certainly go astray.

"Continue in what you have learned and have become convinced of," says Paul to Timothy in 2 Timothy 3:14. And that sounds like excellent advice for us in our day as well, doesn't it? In the last lesson we shall look at the practical details of how to go about it.

The value of all that we have seen so far depends on just one question: do we actually read the Bible? If we fail here, then all we have learned from this book is just so much irrelevance and unreality. After all, what is the point of being convinced of the authority of Scripture if we never place ourselves under its authority by reading it?

It is vital then that we make Bible reading a regular part of life, and that our reading of Scripture is as profitable as it can be. So let's look at the practical steps we can take to get the maximum benefit from reading the Bible.

Feel Free!

We need to make one thing quite clear at the very outset: there is no law about Bible reading. Nowhere are we told how often we should read it. Nor are there any dire warnings in the Bible for those who fail to read it every day. Fears that a day that is not begun with Bible reading is sure to go wrong belong more to superstition than to truth!

Nonetheless, many people assume that daily reading is required of them, with the result that they either feel more or less permanently guilty because they aren't living up to this standard, or they fall into the trap of reading a set portion every day more to satisfy their conscience than to nourish their spiritual appetite.

Bible reading isn't a burden or duty that God has imposed on us. It is much more helpful to view it as David would have done, to judge by what he says in Psalm 119:161b-162:

"...my heart trembles at your word. I rejoice in your promise like one who

...."

As far as he was concerned, reading the Bible was like embarking on a journey where there was every prospect of finding buried treasure! Now that doesn't sound like a very heavy burden, does it?

So let's get down to it! The question is: how?

1. Listen

The early days of the church that we read about in Acts were times of amazing expansion and power. But it can come as quite a shock to realise that these dynamic believers would never be found quietly reading the Bible at home. For they lived before the invention of the printing press, and so they could not have a personal copy of Scripture.

So what did Paul mean when he reminded Timothy in 2 Timothy 3:15 that he had known the Scriptures from infancy? How had he had access to the Scriptures? The answer can be found in 1 Timothy 4:13, where Paul instructs Timothy:

"Until I come, devote yourself to the ....

of ...., to ...., and to ...."

They had access to the Bible because they heard it being read in public and then used as the basis of preaching and teaching. So the only personal copy of the Bible available to them was the one they carried in their memory!

Not for them the luxury of day-dreaming the sermon away! On the contrary: Acts 2:42 tells us that they "*devoted themselves* to the apostles' teaching". The word used there suggests real keenness and attentiveness; they virtually "glued" themselves to the apostles' teaching. What they heard had to be remembered; if they let their minds wander they would have nothing to feed on through the next week. So they listened, retained and thought over what they heard so that they would be able to tell others.

How do we compare with them? Perhaps we need to change our attitude to preaching and teaching from Scripture. The sermon isn't the price we pay for a good time of worship — it is the major reason for gathering together as the church. It can come as a surprise to learn that the early church seems to have put more emphasis on gathering for teaching than they did on gathering for worship. Indeed, they were known as "disciples" or "believers" which are both words that refer to learning.

So we need to be more serious about the teaching that is given to the church, and take positive steps to retain what we hear. This will mean:

(a) **For the preacher:** Read the Scriptures and then teach and apply what they say — no more and no less. A string of anecdotes, inspirational thoughts and jokes may gain a good response, but it will not feed the people.

(b) **For the listeners:** Make an effort to concentrate and listen. Make notes of the main points that you want to remember. Talk about it as a family at home. Pray through the practical outworking of what you have been taught.

If you recognise any tendency to be casual about the preaching of God's Word you would do well to read through and ponder Hebrews 2:1-4. Clearly we need to be more motivated with a sense of high privilege that we are in a position to know what we know.

2. Read

We have an advantage over the early church: we do not have to try to remember so much, as we can own and read the Bible for ourselves. But where do we start, and what should we be wanting to achieve?

A. The time

Time to read the Bible will never present itself ready labelled. As time normally gets filled with a variety of activities and duties, we will need to carve out a usable slot. If we simply wait until we have time, we will probably rarely read the Bible.

So, if we are going to carve out time, we might as well make sure that it is a suitable time. It must be when we are awake, alert and undistracted. It is pointless attempting to benefit from Bible reading if your eyelids are heavy or you are keeping one eye on the television!

B. The method

Where to start and what to read? These are questions that have to be answered — although both are answered for you if you use monthly Bible-reading notes or some other ready-made plan. These schemes have the advantage of guiding you in systematic reading while giving you helpful explanatory notes. A disadvantage is that you can become so tied to the notes that you can be satisfied to complete your daily assignment as quickly as possible and fail to feed on God's Word in any meaningful way.

Basically there are two approaches to Bible reading: the intensive and the extensive approach. If you read intensively, you will tend to study one verse at a time, spend much time thinking about each word and cross-refer to other places in the Bible where the same words or ideas appear. This method makes your progress through the Bible very slow but very rewarding.

In contrast, the extensive reader will read at least a chapter at a time, or possibly a book at a time. Unlike the intensive reader, he will gain a much broader concept of the teaching of Scripture and at a much faster rate. He will miss savouring some of the riches along the way, however.

So each approach has something to be said for it. It is important to get a sense of the overall thrust of a passage and not get so bogged down that it becomes an unconnected sequence of marvellously significant and rich words. On the other hand, it is good to delve into the significance of words and details and not feel pressured to cover as much ground as possible in as short a time as possible. Perhaps the best solution is to combine both methods; read a reasonable chunk at a time, while feeling free to stop and enjoy the view every so often.

C. Understanding it

We will not normally find that wonderful truths leap off the page and demand our attention. It is much more likely that we will have to put some effort into our quest to learn from the Bible.

So let's list some basic principles for understanding what the Bible says.

Meaning. Do you actually understand the meaning of the words you are reading? If you gloss over words about which you are unclear, you are unlikely to gain much from what you are reading. So, why not pick up a dictionary and check up on any words you are not sure of? A problem here is that we can *think* we know what something means until someone asks us about it. So why not act as such a questioner as you read and keep asking yourself what it means?

EXAMPLE: Romans 8:29. To learn from this verse we need to be sure that we understand the meaning of "foreknew", "predestined", "conformed" and "firstborn". Skip these words and you have lost the verse.

Context. Does the setting of the verse you are looking at provide clues as to its meaning and application? It is certainly a very common mistake to overlook this and so make verses say something very different from what was intended.

EXAMPLE: Philippians 4:13. Ignore the setting and you have Paul professing to be able to do anything. Ignore the rest of Scripture, and you could conclude that we are all of us potentially gifted to handle whatever comes. Yet the truth is stated in several places that we each have a measure of faith, and we must therefore admit our need of each other. So what does this verse really mean? Well, the previous verses make it clear: Paul is saying that he has learned to cope with a variety of circumstances. He can be content in poverty or plenty, whether full or hungry. This is what he is referring to when he says he can "do everything".

Interrogate. A way to open a passage up is to question everything. Why this detail? Why did this happen? Why is this word used? etc.

EXAMPLE: Luke 7:11-17. One could simply read the story through, marvel at it and then move on. Or one could ask questions:

- Why are we told the name of the place? Why are we told about the crowds that were there? Possibly because this anchors the story in a specific place among many eyewitnesses who could be questioned about it.
- Any significance in the town gate? The town gate was a centre of activity, and hence again we are aware of many who could corroborate the story — only this time they are people who were not necessarily sympathetic to Jesus.
- Why the details "only son" and "widow"? To underline the tragedy of a woman left with no one to support her. This was what stirred Jesus' compassion.
- What do we learn from the detail that Jesus' "heart went out to her"? We see that Jesus was not just moving according to a divine plan; He felt genuinely for people and was moved by their need.
- Why did he tell her not to cry?
- What is the significance of Jesus touching the coffin?
- Can you think of anyone else who gave a son back to his mother?
- Are the people reminded of this when they call Jesus a "prophet"?

(You can answer these last four questions yourself, and then come up with many more!)

Avoid the fanciful. Don't get from your reading things that other ordinary people would not find there. If you read things into the Bible, you are drifting away from the Word of God into ideas that you have concocted yourself. It is safer to stick to the plain meaning of Scripture, and not to look for hidden meanings.

EXAMPLE: 1 Samuel 17:40. This verse tells us that David "chose five smooth stones from the stream". There have been preachers who have expounded this verse by considering what these stones stood for. There are two flaws to this line of thinking. First, having decided the five essentials for warfare, or whatever you decide the stones stood for, you have to face the fact that only one was needed and the rest were thrown back! A more significant flaw is this: those stones stood for nothing other than what they were — five smooth stones. The story is clearly a statement of what happened; it is not a parable.

A danger in such fanciful interpretations is that you can confuse your own thoughts with what God says and quote your interpretation as if the Bible says it. This can happen particularly with interpretations of passages that speak about the end times and events that are still to happen. Be careful!

Acquire tools. There are a variety of helpful "tools" to enrich our study of the Bible. It is worth getting a Bible with good references either in the centre of the page or at the foot. These will enable you to find other passages that relate with the one you are reading so that you can follow up lines of thought.

If you want to take this sort of thing further, then it could be worth getting a concordance that matches your version of the Bible.

To help explain difficult passages, it can be good to be able to turn to a commentary. There are many of these in print, ranging from one-volume commentaries on the entire Bible to individual commentaries of varying depth on particular books. The leader of your church ought to be able to suggest what would be best for you.

Then many like to highlight verses or mark the page in other ways. There isn't much point in just highlighting or underlining what you think is good; sooner or later most of it will be underlined, which rather defeats the object! But it is helpful to, say, have a fine-point pen so that you can note helpful references and other information alongside the relevant verse. Or you may like to have a set of highlighter pencils to develop a system of colour coding particular themes through the Bible. But remember, the object isn't to be clever, but to feed on God's Word.

3. Do

In John 13 we read of an occasion when Jesus was teaching His disciples some vital principles. He ended with the words that are recorded in v.17:

"Now that you know these things, you will be .... if you
.... "

If you take your Bible seriously, your knowledge about God and His will for your life will certainly increase. What matters then is that you should do what you have learned.

We read the Bible not just to enlarge our mind but to enrich our life. We need to identify the "therefore" of the truth we see, and do it. There is little to be gained from joining the ranks of theoretical Christians: those who know what ought to happen but never put anything into practice.

Find James 1:22. What does James say we are doing to ourselves if we fail to act on what we hear from the Bible?

We .... ourselves.

Many are self-deceived about what they think they know. We only *really* know what we have proved in experience. To have merely heard and agreed with something isn't enough.

How do you think you rate on this? Let's find out! First of all, think back and note down four things you have been taught about over the past four weeks.

1. ....

2. ....

3. ....

4. ....

Now make a note of what you have actually *done* as a result of this teaching:

1. ....

2. ....

3. ....

4. ....

Are you just a "hearer", or are you a "hearer and doer"? God looks for those who both hear and *do* what He says.

4. Think

Our time with the Bible doesn't end when we close the book. Do you remember what we saw about those first-century Christians? They fed on the Scriptures by remembering what was read to them; the Word of God was stored in their minds. When the apostles quoted the Old Testament, they did so from memory. And when they expounded its significance in the light of what they now knew about Jesus, they did so because they had thought it through in their minds.

So we need to retain the substance of what we read and hear, and think about it often. We will then find that we are seeing its relevance to everyday situations. So we are helped to develop Biblical attitudes and behaviour.

We sometimes use the expression "feeding" on God's Word. Well, it is a most unusual form of nourishment, because we can keep chewing it over right through the day in order to get the maximum enjoyment and benefit from it!

Do you do this? You can check yourself by looking back over the list you have just made of things you have heard being taught over the past four weeks. Now write down what you have seen about these subjects *since* you heard them taught:

1. ....

2. ....

3. ....

4. ....

Is your mind actually being renewed by what you learn from Scripture, or is it possibly unaffected by what you hear? If you realise that you have adjustments to make in this, then ask God to help you, and start to use your mind.

Finally

It really is an amazing privilege that God should ever have spoken to us. No wonder people have given their lives for this wonderful book, to preserve it and make it available to all who want access to it!

The Bible is a book which will never be outdated. Nothing better is going to come our way — until we see God Himself face to face. It will always bring the wisdom of God to us so that we are "thoroughly equipped for every good work" (2 Timothy 3:16-17). It will always "teach, rebuke, correct and train in righteousness."

Therefore, we are wise if we resolve to treasure it and submit to it come what may. Satan will always find ways of putting in one form or another the question, "Did God really say ...?" (Genesis 3:1). What we have seen in this book should be enough to enable us to be sure of our ground as we resist his insidious challenges. So, like Jesus, we can confidently reply: "It is written ..."!